My Ramadan

ACTIVITY BOOK

Published by LeNoble Publishing

First edition; First Printing

Copyright © 2022 Heidi van 't Riet

ISBN: 978-1-955132-16-9

THIS BOOK BELONGS TO

I am

years old

My Friends Are

_____
_____
_____
_____

My Favorite

color: _____
food: _____
animal: _____

I like to watch

i live with _____

in _____

Books:

I am good at

_____
_____
_____

Favorite Activities

_____
_____
_____
_____
_____
_____

When I Grow Up I Want To Be...

_____
_____

My Goals for Ramadan   اهدافي في رمضان

_____

_____

_____

_____

_____

_____

_____

_____

_____

_____

_____

_____

_____

_____

_____

_____

_____

_____

_____

_____

_____

Welcome!

مرحباً

This journal is designed to help you reflect on and enjoy the holy month of Ramadan.

Inside the journal, you will find 2 pages for each day of Ramadan. On one page you will find several trackers. The fasting tracker across the top of the page lets you show how far through the day you completed your fast. The prayer tracker lets you check off the completion of your prayers each day. And the water tracker helps you make sure that you drink enough water after you break your fast so you don't get dehydrated.

On this page, you'll also find a journal prompt - a different one for each day. The journal prompts give you the opportunity to think about the meaning of the month from a lot of different angles.

On the second page for each day, you'll find an activity like a coloring sheet or a puzzle. In case you need instructions for the puzzles, they are in the back of the book. If the puzzle has an answer, you'll also find that in the back of the book.

After the daily pages, you'll find a few pages with some games you can play with someone else. It's always fun to spend some time with the people you care about playing a game.

At the end of Ramadan, you'll have a wonderful momento of the month, something you can keep for years. You'll be able to see your progress through the month and through the years.

Ramadan Kareem!

رمضان كريم

MY FASTING

6am 7am 8am 9am 10am 11am 12pm

Ramadan 1

رمضان ١

DATE التاريخ

SUNRISE الشروق

SUNSET الغروب

What are your goals for Ramadan? What is one thing you can do today to start working towards the goals?

_____

_____

_____

_____

_____

_____

my prayers
صلاتي

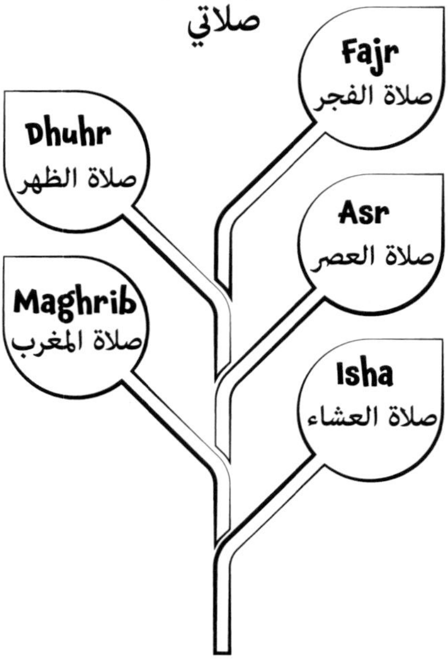

Fajr
صلاة الفجر

Dhuhr
صلاة الظهر

Asr
صلاة العصر

Maghrib
صلاة المغرب

Isha
صلاة العشاء

my water
عدد اكواب الماء

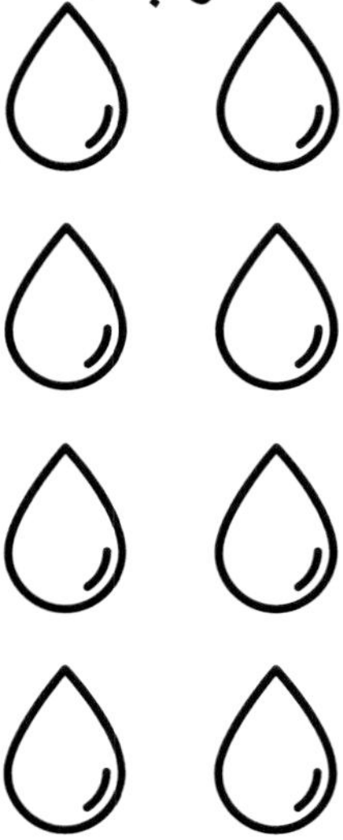

MY FASTING

6am 7am 8am 9am 10am 11am 12pm

Ramadan 2

رمضان٢

DATE التاريخ

SUNRISE الشروق

SUNSET الغروب

What do you know about the month of Ramadan? What else would you like to learn about it?

_____

_____

_____

_____

_____

_____

my prayers
صلاتي

Fajr
صلاة الفجر

Dhuhr
صلاة الظهر

Asr
صلاة العصر

Maghrib
صلاة المغرب

Isha
صلاة العشاء

my water
عدد اكواب الماء

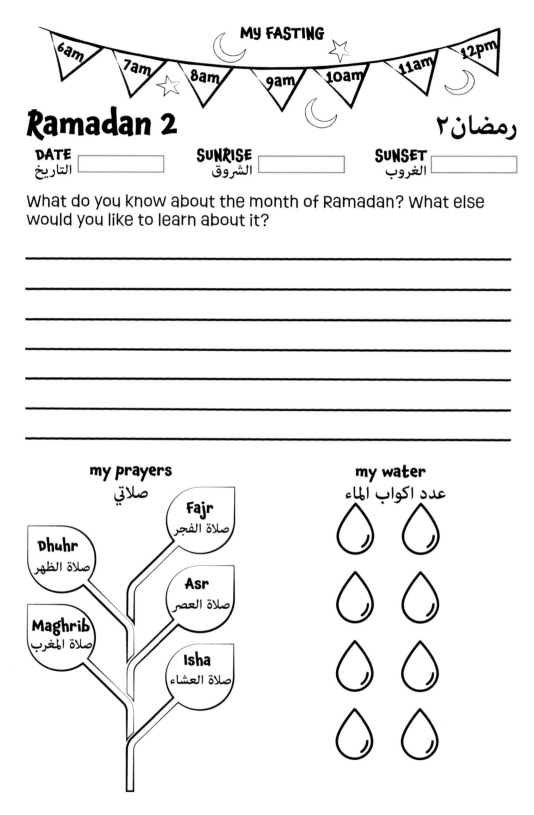

Ramadan 3

رمضان٣

DATE التاريخ [ ]   **SUNRISE** الشروق [ ]   **SUNSET** الغروب [ ]

Create an iftar menu. Sketch your meal.

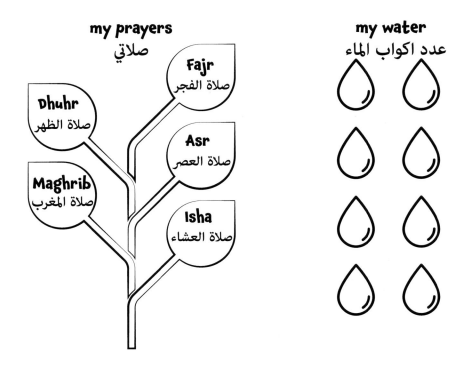

my prayers
صلاتي

Fajr صلاة الفجر

Dhuhr صلاة الظهر

Asr صلاة العصر

Maghrib صلاة المغرب

Isha صلاة العشاء

my water
عدد اكواب الماء

Help the boy find his lamp.

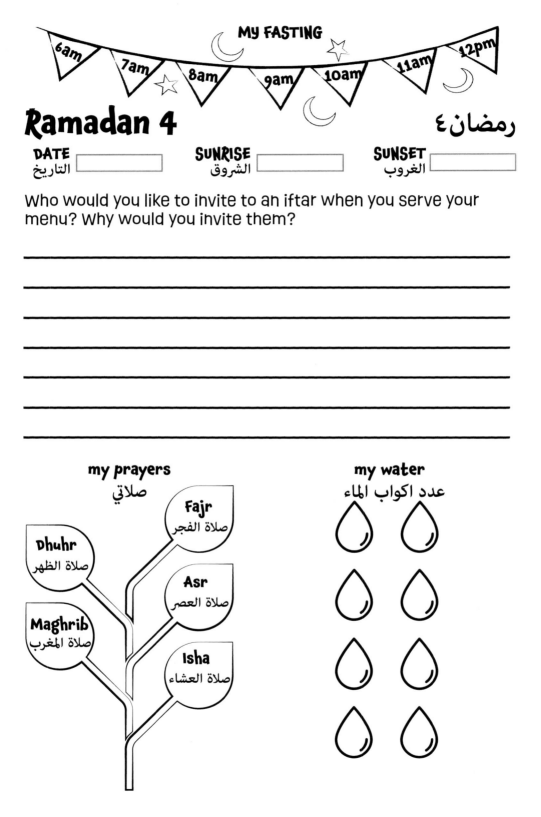

MY FASTING

6am 7am 8am 9am 10am 11am 12pm

Ramadan 4

رمضان ٤

DATE
التاريخ

SUNRISE
الشروق

SUNSET
الغروب

Who would you like to invite to an iftar when you serve your menu? Why would you invite them?

_____

_____

_____

_____

_____

_____

my prayers
صلاتي

Fajr
صلاة الفجر

Dhuhr
صلاة الظهر

Asr
صلاة العصر

Maghrib
صلاة المغرب

Isha
صلاة العشاء

my water
عدد اكواب الماء

Sudoku

If you don't know how to do Sudoku puzzles, there are instructions in the back of the book.
Answers are also in the back of the book.

puzzle 1

3		6	5		1	4		9
		4	7		3		2	8
2		7		4		5		
9		5		8	2		6	4
8	4	3	1	6		2	9	7
6	1	2		7	4			3
4	3			5	9	7	8	6
	2	8			6		1	
5			8			3	4	2

puzzle 2

2	5	6	8	9	1	3		
		7		4	6	5	1	9
9	1		7			8	6	2
1	9	3	5					
				6		1	9	
	6		1	2	9	7	5	
3	2	1		5	8		7	4
7	8		6	1	4		3	5
6	4	5				9	8	1

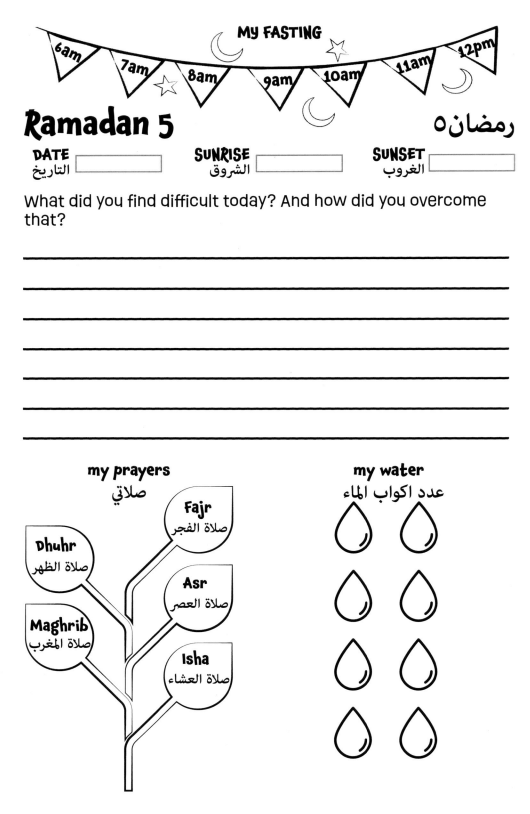

MY FASTING

6am 7am 8am 9am 10am 11am 12pm

Ramadan 5
رمضان٥

DATE التاريخ

SUNRISE الشروق

SUNSET الغروب

What did you find difficult today? And how did you overcome that?

_____

_____

_____

_____

_____

_____

_____

my prayers
صلاتي

Fajr صلاة الفجر

Dhuhr صلاة الظهر

Asr صلاة العصر

Maghrib صلاة المغرب

Isha صلاة العشاء

my water
عدد اكواب الماء

KenKen

If you don't know how to do KenKen puzzles, there are instructions in the back of the book.
Answers are also in the back of the book.

puzzle 1

2 -		1 -	5 +
8 +	5 +		
		6 +	
	5 +		

puzzle 2

8 +	2 -		7 +
		5 +	
2 -			
2 -		2 -	

puzzle 3

5 +	1 -		5 +
		1 -	
5 +			5 +
8 +			

puzzle 4

2 -		1 -	13 +
1 -			
1 -	2 -		
		2 -	

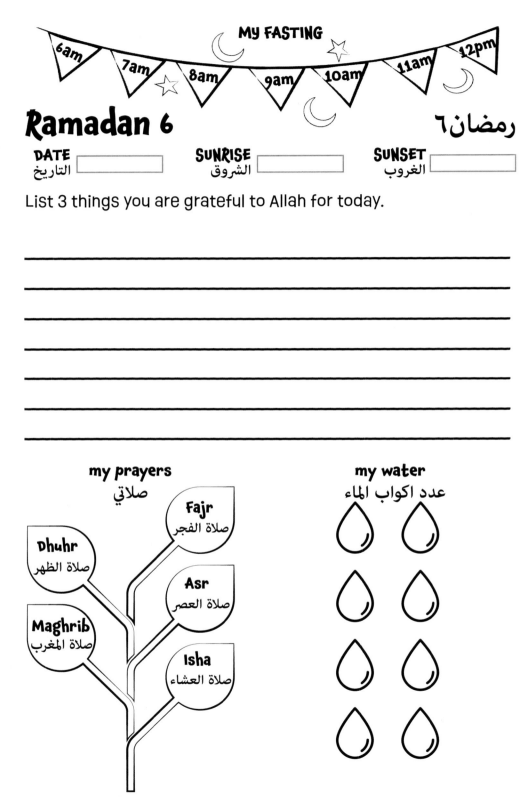

MY FASTING

6am 7am 8am 9am 10am 11am 12pm

Ramadan 6

رمضان ٦

DATE
التاريخ

SUNRISE
الشروق

SUNSET
الغروب

List 3 things you are grateful to Allah for today.

_____

_____

_____

_____

_____

_____

_____

my prayers
صلاتي

Fajr
صلاة الفجر

Dhuhr
صلاة الظهر

Asr
صلاة العصر

Maghrib
صلاة المغرب

Isha
صلاة العشاء

my water
عدد اكواب الماء

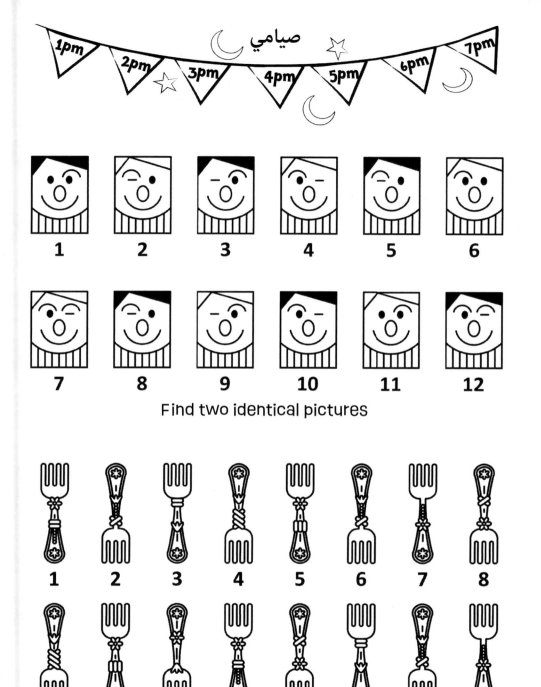

صيامي

Find two identical pictures

Which fork is unique?

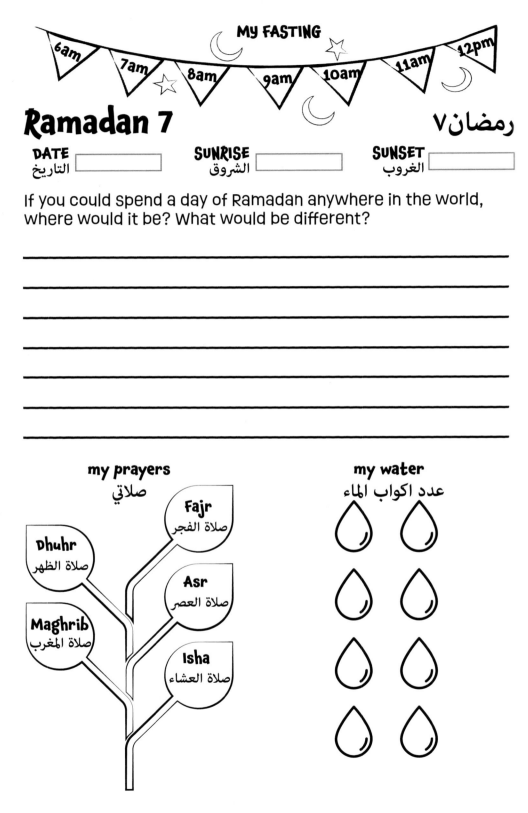

MY FASTING

6am 7am 8am 9am 10am 11am 12pm

Ramadan 7

رمضان٧

DATE التاريخ

SUNRISE الشروق

SUNSET الغروب

If you could spend a day of Ramadan anywhere in the world, where would it be? What would be different?

_____

_____

_____

_____

_____

_____

my prayers
صلاتي

Fajr
صلاة الفجر

Dhuhr
صلاة الظهر

Asr
صلاة العصر

Maghrib
صلاة المغرب

Isha
صلاة العشاء

my water
عدد اكواب الماء

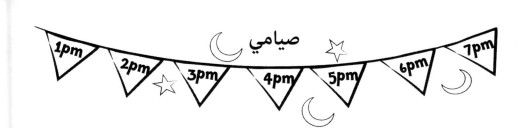

صيامي

MY FASTING

6am 7am 8am 9am 10am 11am 12pm

Ramadan 8

رمضان٨

DATE
التاريخ

SUNRISE
الشروق

SUNSET
الغروب

What did you do well today? How did that make you feel?

_____

_____

_____

_____

_____

_____

_____

my prayers
صلاتي

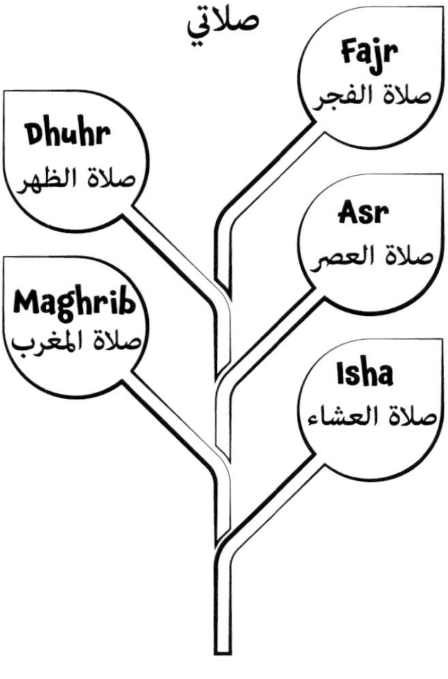

Fajr
صلاة الفجر

Dhuhr
صلاة الظهر

Asr
صلاة العصر

Maghrib
صلاة المغرب

Isha
صلاة العشاء

my water
عدد اكواب الماء

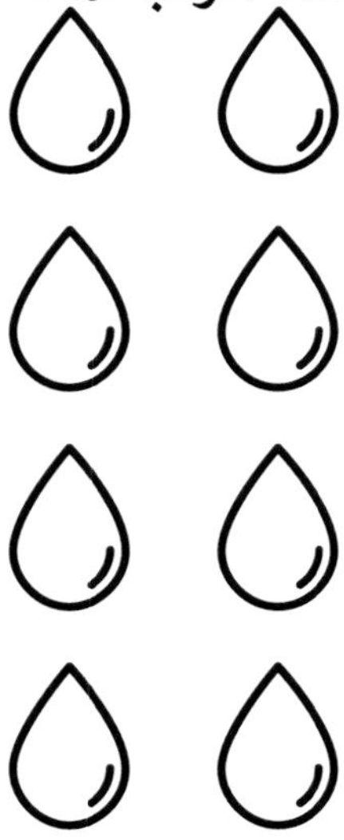

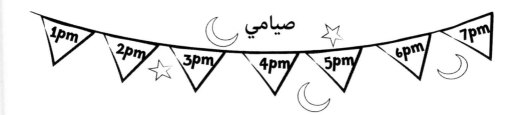

Find your way from the the star out to the edge.

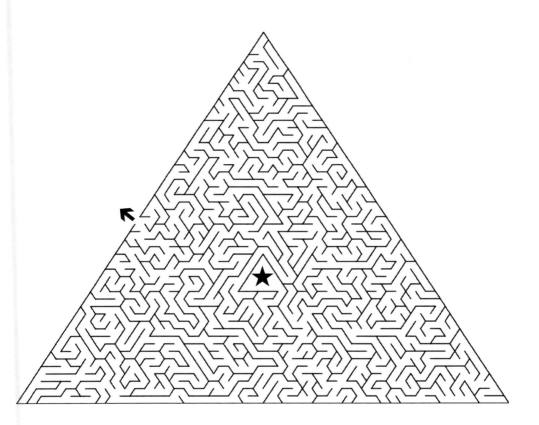

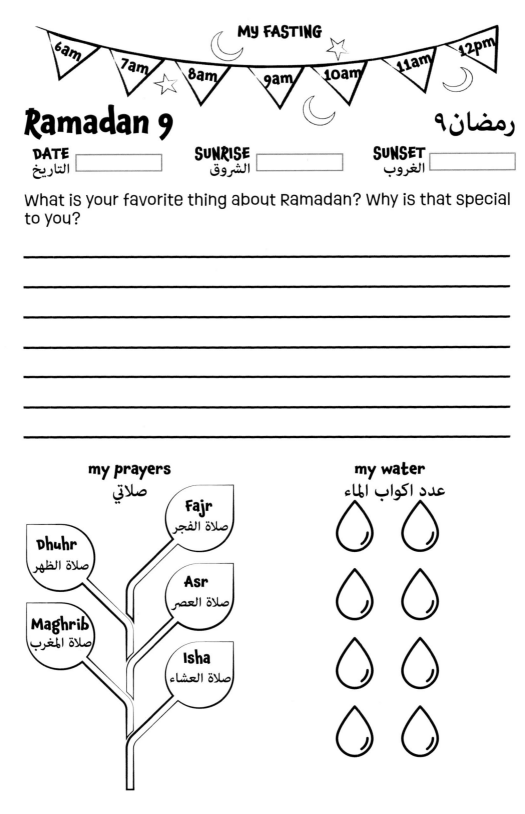

MY FASTING

6am 7am 8am 9am 10am 11am 12pm

Ramadan 9

رمضان٩

DATE
التاريخ

SUNRISE
الشروق

SUNSET
الغروب

What is your favorite thing about Ramadan? Why is that special to you?

_____

_____

_____

_____

_____

_____

my prayers
صلاتي

Fajr
صلاة الفجر

Dhuhr
صلاة الظهر

Asr
صلاة العصر

Maghrib
صلاة المغرب

Isha
صلاة العشاء

my water
عدد اكواب الماء

Math Picture Puzzle

If you don't know how to do math picture puzzles, there are instructions in the back of the book.
Answers are also in the back of the book.

📖 X 📖 = 25

📖 + 🕌 = 8

🧧 - 🕌 = 9

📖 + 🧧 = ?

🧧 X 🧧 = 49

🧧 + 🕌 = 11

💥 - 🕌 = 1

🧧 + 💥 = ?

Ramadan 10

رمضان ١٠

DATE
التاريخ

SUNRISE
الشروق

SUNSET
الغروب

If you could describe today with one word, what word would you choose? Why did you choose that word?

_____

_____

_____

_____

_____

_____

my prayers
صلاتي

Fajr
صلاة الفجر

Dhuhr
صلاة الظهر

Asr
صلاة العصر

Maghrib
صلاة المغرب

Isha
صلاة العشاء

my water
عدد اكواب الماء

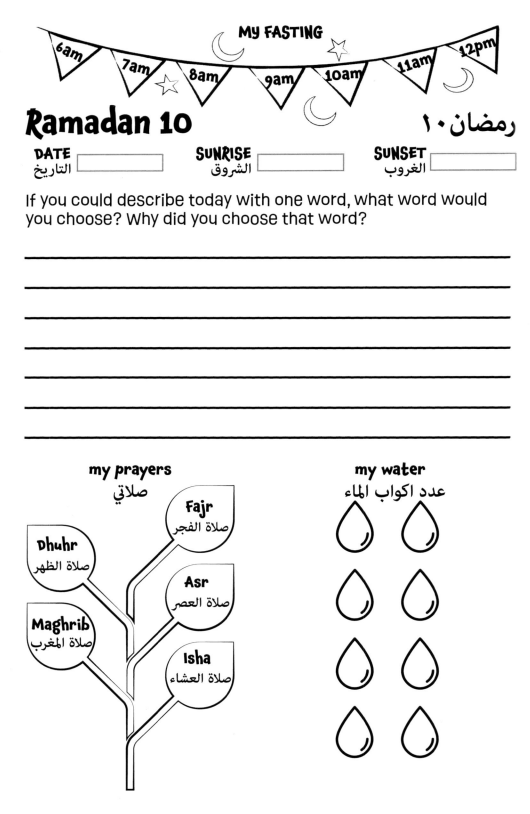

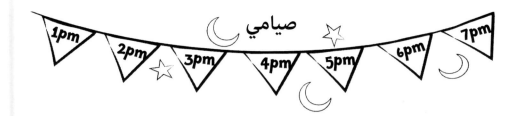

صيامي

Find the two identical pictures.

Spot the five differences.

MY FASTING

6am 7am 8am 9am 10am 11am 12pm

Ramadan 11

رمضان ١١

DATE
التاريخ

SUNRISE
الشروق

SUNSET
الغروب

What is your favorite Ramadan memory? What makes that memory so special?

_____

_____

_____

_____

_____

_____

my prayers
صلاتي

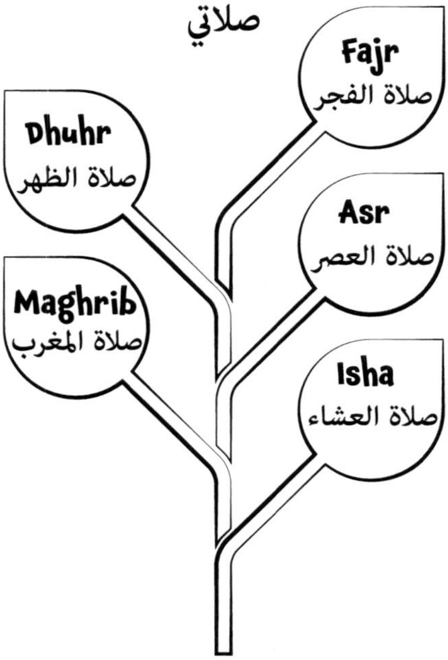

Fajr
صلاة الفجر

Dhuhr
صلاة الظهر

Asr
صلاة العصر

Maghrib
صلاة المغرب

Isha
صلاة العشاء

my water
عدد اكواب الماء

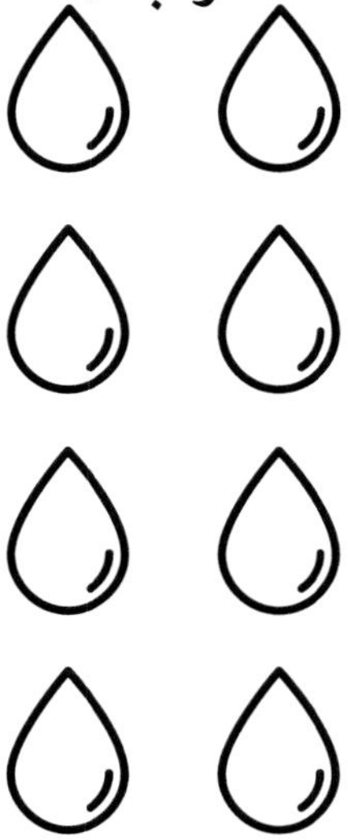

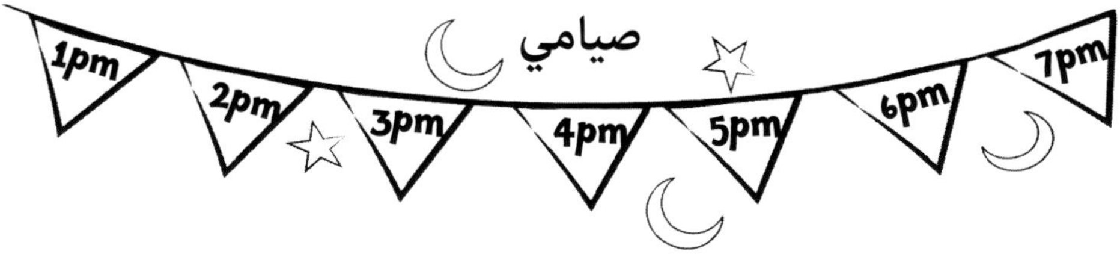

صيامي

1pm 2pm 3pm 4pm 5pm 6pm 7pm

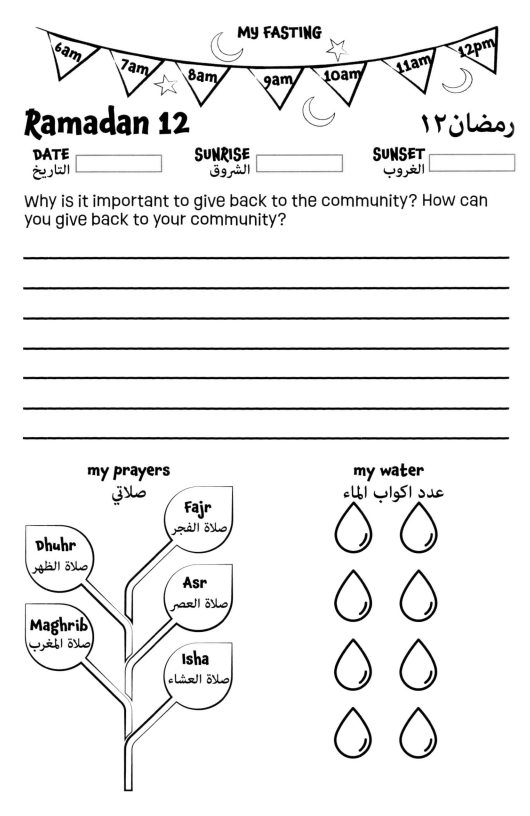

MY FASTING

6am 7am 8am 9am 10am 11am 12pm

Ramadan 12

رمضان١٢

DATE
التاريخ

SUNRISE
الشروق

SUNSET
الغروب

Why is it important to give back to the community? How can you give back to your community?

_____

_____

_____

_____

_____

_____

my prayers
صلاتي

Fajr
صلاة الفجر

Dhuhr
صلاة الظهر

Asr
صلاة العصر

Maghrib
صلاة المغرب

Isha
صلاة العشاء

my water
عدد اكواب الماء

صيامي

1pm 2pm 3pm 4pm 5pm 6pm 7pm

puzzle 3

		6					7	3
	7	3	6	4	8		2	5
	2		7	3	1			8
	9	4	3			8	1	7
3	8		4	6			5	
	5	7	8		9			6
7	1	5		8		3	6	2
4	6	8		5			9	
9	3	2		7	6	5	8	4

puzzle 4

	2	1				9	7	
3	5	7	9		6		8	4
9	6	8			1	5	2	3
6	4		3	1		8	5	7
	1	3		4	5			9
5			6		7	4	3	
8	7		1					
1		6		5		7	9	
2		4	7	8	3	6	1	5

Ramadan 13

رمضان ١٣

DATE
التاريخ

SUNRISE
الشروق

SUNSET
الغروب

What are your family traditions during Ramadan? Write about a time when your family practiced this tradition and how it made you feel.

_____

_____

_____

_____

_____

_____

my prayers
صلاتي

Fajr
صلاة الفجر

Dhuhr
صلاة الظهر

Asr
صلاة العصر

Maghrib
صلاة المغرب

Isha
صلاة العشاء

my water
عدد اكواب الماء

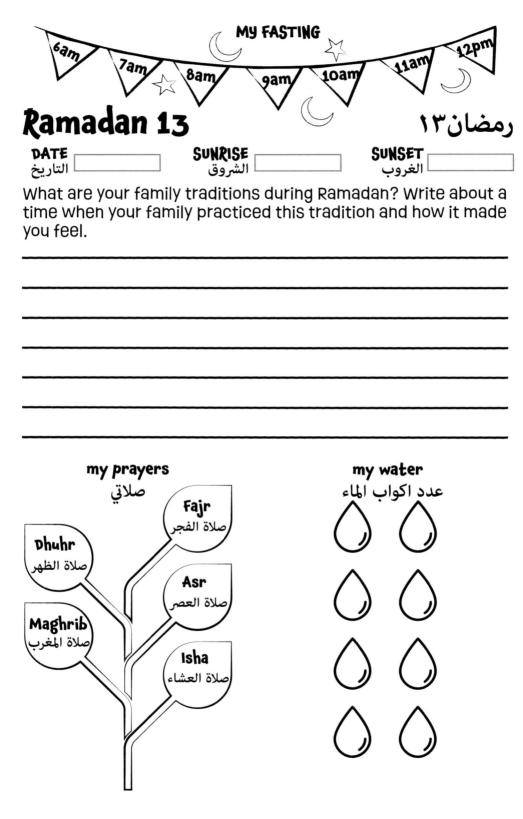

Find the path from the boy to his prayer mat.

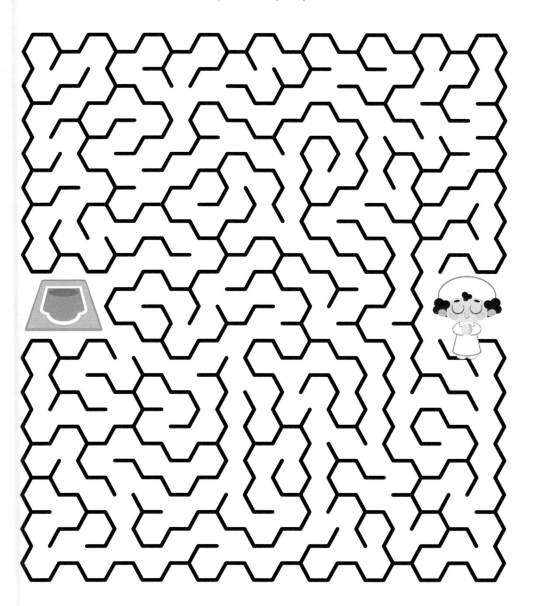

MY FASTING

6am 7am 8am 9am 10am 11am 12pm

Ramadan 14

رمضان ١٤

DATE التاريخ

SUNRISE الشروق

SUNSET الغروب

Interview someone in your family about what makes Ramadan special to them.

_____

_____

_____

_____

_____

_____

_____

my prayers
صلاتي

Fajr
صلاة الفجر

Dhuhr
صلاة الظهر

Asr
صلاة العصر

Maghrib
صلاة المغرب

Isha
صلاة العشاء

my water
عدد اكواب الماء

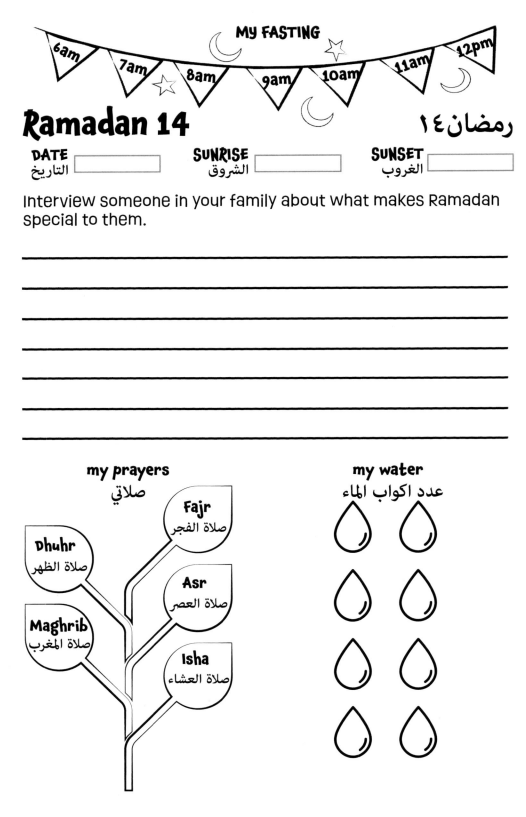

صيامي

KenKen

puzzle 5

1 -		5 +	
7 +	2 -		2 -
	2 -	9 +	

puzzle 6

2 -	8 +	1 -	
		2 -	9 +
2 -			
	2 -		

puzzle 7

8 +			2 -
4 +	1 -		
		11 +	
2 -			

puzzle 8

1 -	8 +	1 -	
		2 -	
1 -		4 +	
	5 +		

Ramadan 15

رمضان ١٥

DATE التاريخ [　　　　　] **SUNRISE** الشروق [　　　　　] **SUNSET** الغروب [　　　　　]

Write a thank you letter to someone who has made a difference in your life. Tell them how they have affected you and what they mean to you.

_____

_____

_____

_____

_____

_____

my prayers
صلاتي

Fajr صلاة الفجر

Dhuhr صلاة الظهر

Asr صلاة العصر

Maghrib صلاة المغرب

Isha صلاة العشاء

my water
عدد اكواب الماء

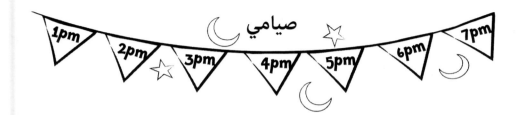

Which mug is unique?

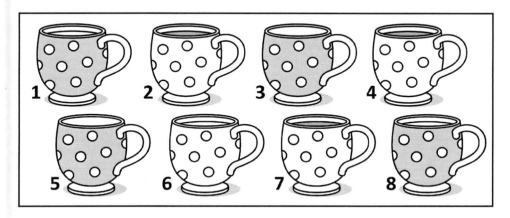

Can you find five differences?

MY FASTING

6am 7am 8am 9am 10am 11am 12pm

Ramadan 16

رمضان ١٦

DATE التاريخ

SUNRISE الشروق

SUNSET الغروب

What is the most valuable lesson you've learned about Ramadan this month? Why is that interesting?

_____

_____

_____

_____

_____

_____

my prayers
صلاتي

Fajr
صلاة الفجر

Dhuhr
صلاة الظهر

Asr
صلاة العصر

Maghrib
صلاة المغرب

Isha
صلاة العشاء

my water
عدد اكواب الماء

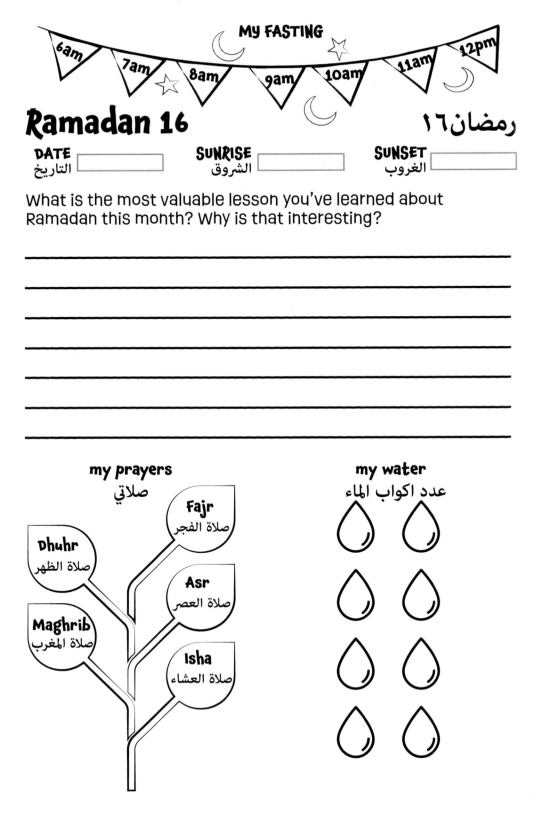

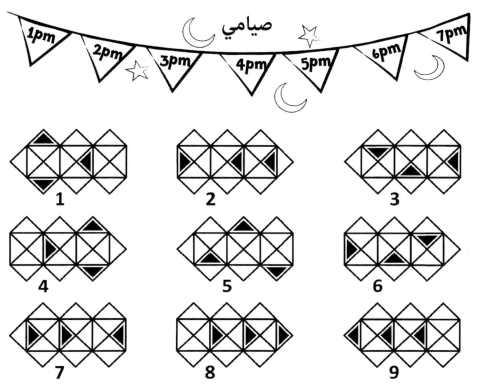

Spot the object that has no mirrored copy

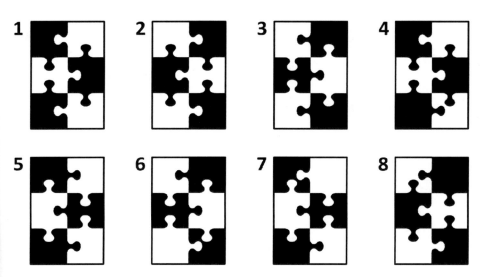

Match the negatives to the positives

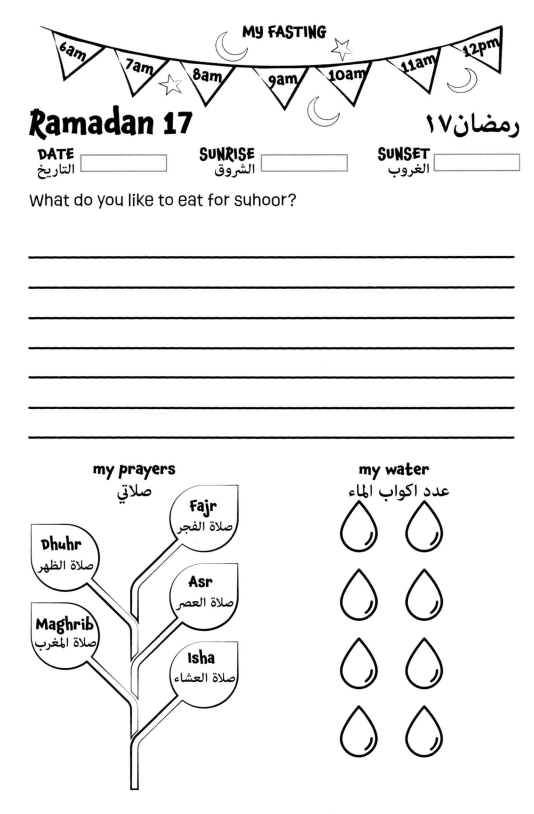

MY FASTING

6am 7am 8am 9am 10am 11am 12pm

Ramadan 17

رمضان ١٧

DATE
التاريخ

SUNRISE
الشروق

SUNSET
الغروب

What do you like to eat for suhoor?

_____

_____

_____

_____

_____

_____

my prayers
صلاتي

Fajr
صلاة الفجر

Dhuhr
صلاة الظهر

Asr
صلاة العصر

Maghrib
صلاة المغرب

Isha
صلاة العشاء

my water
عدد اكواب الماء

🔫 X 🔫 = 144

🔫 + 🧧 = 23

🧧 − 🏮 = 8

🔫 + 🏮 = ?

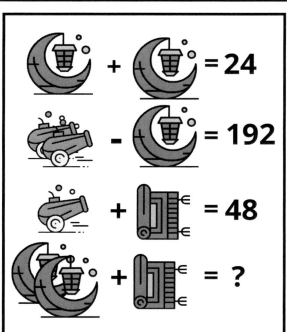

🏮 + 🏮 = 24

🔫 − 🏮 = 192

🔫 + 🧧 = 48

🏮 + 🧧 = ?

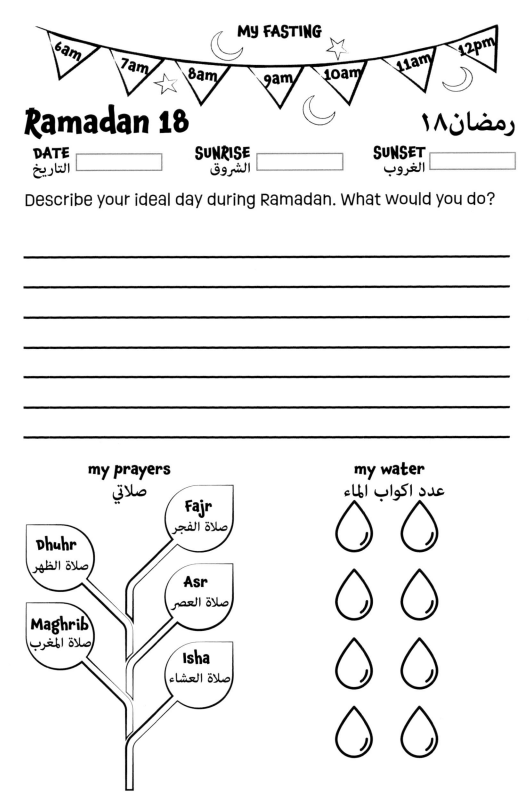

MY FASTING

6am 7am 8am 9am 10am 11am 12pm

Ramadan 18

رمضان ١٨

DATE التاريخ

SUNRISE الشروق

SUNSET الغروب

Describe your ideal day during Ramadan. What would you do?

_____

_____

_____

_____

_____

_____

my prayers
صلاتي

Fajr
صلاة الفجر

Dhuhr
صلاة الظهر

Asr
صلاة العصر

Maghrib
صلاة المغرب

Isha
صلاة العشاء

my water
عدد اكواب الماء

puzzle 5

	2	3	8	1	9	5		6
	8			5	2	3	9	
5	9	6	3	4	7	2	8	
9	5	8		3		4	2	7
	6		7	9				8
		7	2			9		5
	7		5	2	1	8		
	4		9		3	7	1	2
	3		4		8		5	9

puzzle 6

7		3	4	8				
2	8	1		5	6		7	
		4				9	2	
8	7		5		3		4	9
1	2	5	7	4			8	
4		9	1		8	7	5	
3	4		2		5		9	6
5				9	4	2	3	7
9		2	8	3	7	4	1	5

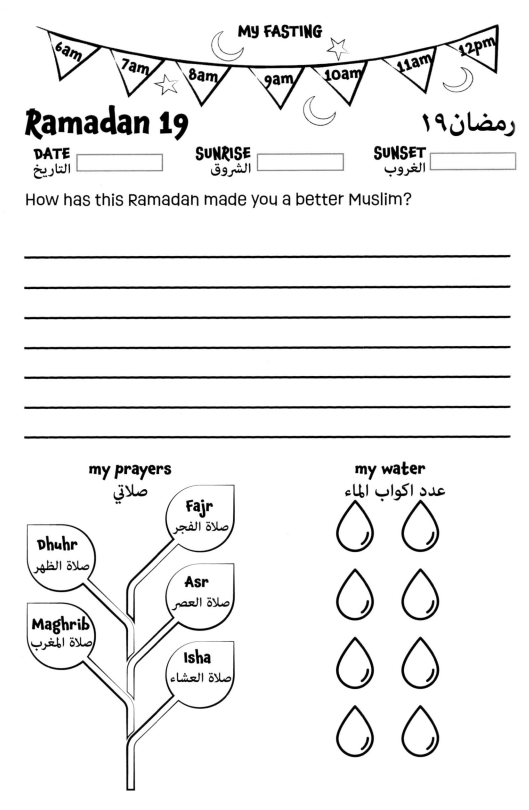

MY FASTING

6am 7am 8am 9am 10am 11am 12pm

Ramadan 19

رمضان ١٩

DATE
التاريخ

SUNRISE
الشروق

SUNSET
الغروب

How has this Ramadan made you a better Muslim?

_____

_____

_____

_____

_____

_____

my prayers
صلاتي

Fajr
صلاة الفجر

Dhuhr
صلاة الظهر

Asr
صلاة العصر

Maghrib
صلاة المغرب

Isha
صلاة العشاء

my water
عدد اكواب الماء

Word Search

```
W U T E O W H H Z H E L L D R C
U L W H I T J V U M C V A Q P I
U B E E I Y A Z S X M A J L U I
G B X A L E I D A L F I T R C U
B B F I X N T Q U R A N K B T F
V S M A S U F R I E N D S X D N
C A Q C U L E J D A E L L X O E
F M R C H G A U B F S K J O Q L
U U T P F A T M P R A N M K K L
H S I M R I R F O A A S U V W I
D L W M T A J I I A T M T L K U
W I X A S P Y U T F P I A I X U
Q M R H U A G E K Y T A E D N N
H G Y P B A S V R C H A O N A G
Q F W W U H H P O C I S R Q C N
Q G B Y I M B P P Z K Q Z E X E
```

CHARITY	EID AL FITR	FAITH
FAMILY	FASTING	FRIENDS
GRATITUDE	IFTAR	ISLAM
MOON	MUSLIM	PATIENCE
PRAYER	QURAN	RAMADAN

MY FASTING

6am 7am 8am 9am 10am 11am 12pm

Ramadan 20

رمضان ٢٠

DATE التاريخ

SUNRISE الشروق

SUNSET الغروب

How are you progressing towards your goals? What is one thing you can do tomorrow to keep moving toward your goals?

_____

_____

_____

_____

_____

_____

my prayers
صلاتي

Fajr صلاة الفجر

Dhuhr صلاة الظهر

Asr صلاة العصر

Maghrib صلاة المغرب

Isha صلاة العشاء

my water
عدد اكواب الماء

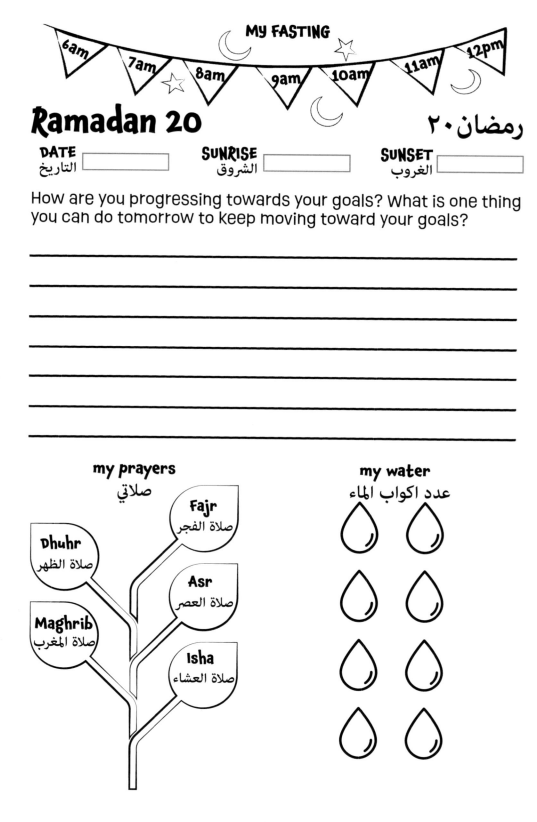

KenKen

puzzle 9

32 ×		75 ×		
2 -		5 +		
	2 -	3 -		96 ×
3 -		6 +		
	2 /			

puzzle 10

2 /	40 ×			7 +
	15 ×			
1 -	5 +		3 -	
	15 ×		7 +	2 /
2 -				

puzzle 11

2 /	5 +		2 -	1 -
	2 /	2 -		
12 ×			2 ×	5 +
	1 -			
15 ×		7 +		

puzzle 12

7 +		8 +		
12 ×	5 ×		2 -	11 +
	2 -	2 /		
1 -			10 ×	
	1 -			

MY FASTING

6am 7am 8am 9am 10am 11am 12pm

Ramadan 21

رمضان ٢١

DATE
التاريخ

SUNRISE
الشروق

SUNSET
الغروب

Help someone else by offering to do a chore at home. How did the other person react?

_____

_____

_____

_____

_____

_____

_____

my prayers
صلاتي

Fajr صلاة الفجر

Dhuhr صلاة الظهر

Asr صلاة العصر

Maghrib صلاة المغرب

Isha صلاة العشاء

my water
عدد اكواب الماء

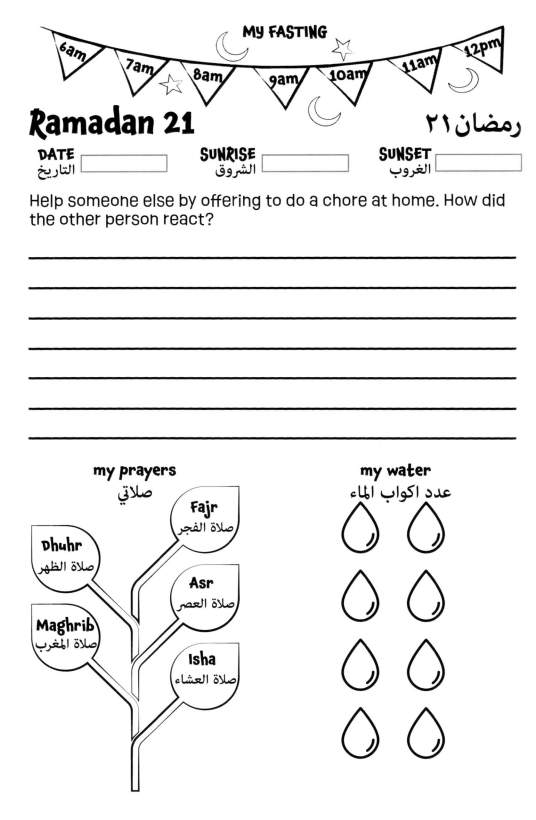

صيامي

MY FASTING

6am 7am 8am 9am 10am 11am 12pm

Ramadan 22

رمضان ٢٢

DATE التاريخ [＿＿＿＿＿]

SUNRISE الشروق [＿＿＿＿＿]

SUNSET الغروب [＿＿＿＿＿]

Write down an ayah/dua/surah that you memorized perfectly. In your own words, what does it mean?

＿＿＿＿＿＿＿＿＿＿＿＿＿＿＿＿＿＿＿＿＿＿＿＿＿＿＿＿＿＿＿

＿＿＿＿＿＿＿＿＿＿＿＿＿＿＿＿＿＿＿＿＿＿＿＿＿＿＿＿＿＿＿

＿＿＿＿＿＿＿＿＿＿＿＿＿＿＿＿＿＿＿＿＿＿＿＿＿＿＿＿＿＿＿

＿＿＿＿＿＿＿＿＿＿＿＿＿＿＿＿＿＿＿＿＿＿＿＿＿＿＿＿＿＿＿

＿＿＿＿＿＿＿＿＿＿＿＿＿＿＿＿＿＿＿＿＿＿＿＿＿＿＿＿＿＿＿

＿＿＿＿＿＿＿＿＿＿＿＿＿＿＿＿＿＿＿＿＿＿＿＿＿＿＿＿＿＿＿

＿＿＿＿＿＿＿＿＿＿＿＿＿＿＿＿＿＿＿＿＿＿＿＿＿＿＿＿＿＿＿

my prayers
صلاتي

Fajr صلاة الفجر

Dhuhr صلاة الظهر

Asr صلاة العصر

Maghrib صلاة المغرب

Isha صلاة العشاء

my water
عدد اكواب الماء

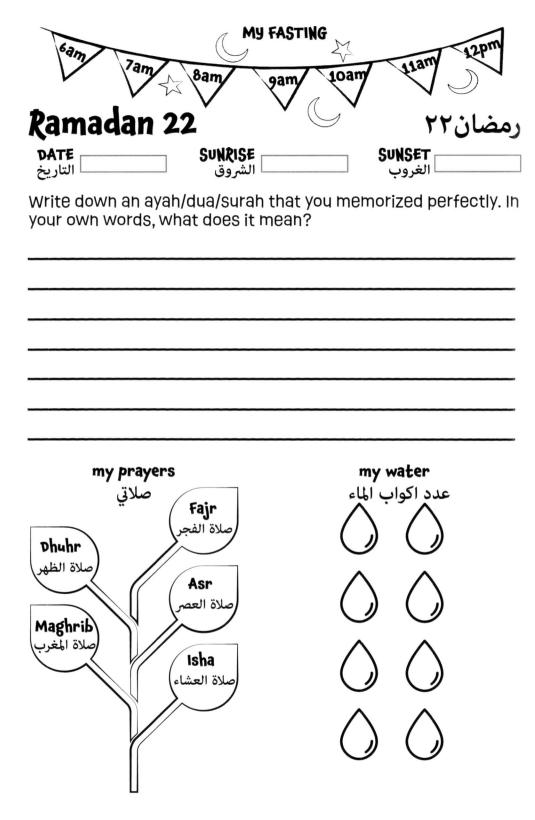

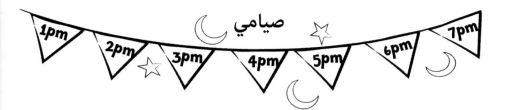

Match the halves. Which number is the smallest?

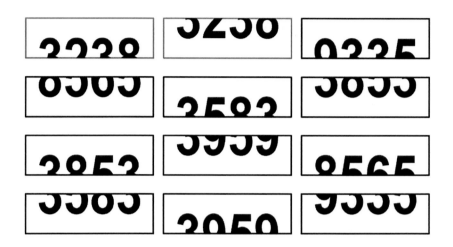

Which picture is the mirror image of picture #1?

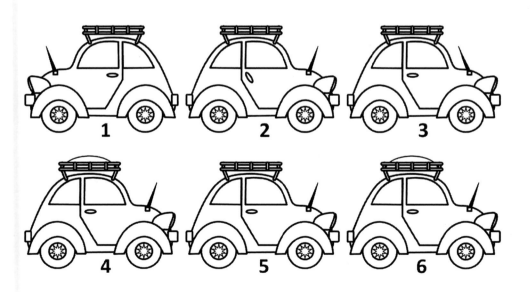

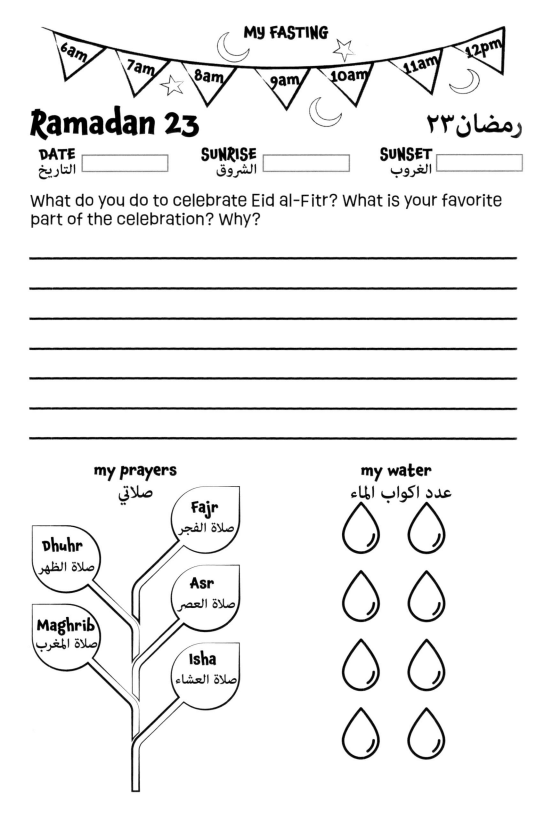

MY FASTING

6am 7am 8am 9am 10am 11am 12pm

Ramadan 23

رمضان ٢٣

DATE التاريخ

SUNRISE الشروق

SUNSET الغروب

What do you do to celebrate Eid al-Fitr? What is your favorite part of the celebration? Why?

_____

_____

_____

_____

_____

_____

_____

my prayers
صلاتي

Fajr صلاة الفجر

Dhuhr صلاة الظهر

Asr صلاة العصر

Maghrib صلاة المغرب

Isha صلاة العشاء

my water
عدد اكواب الماء

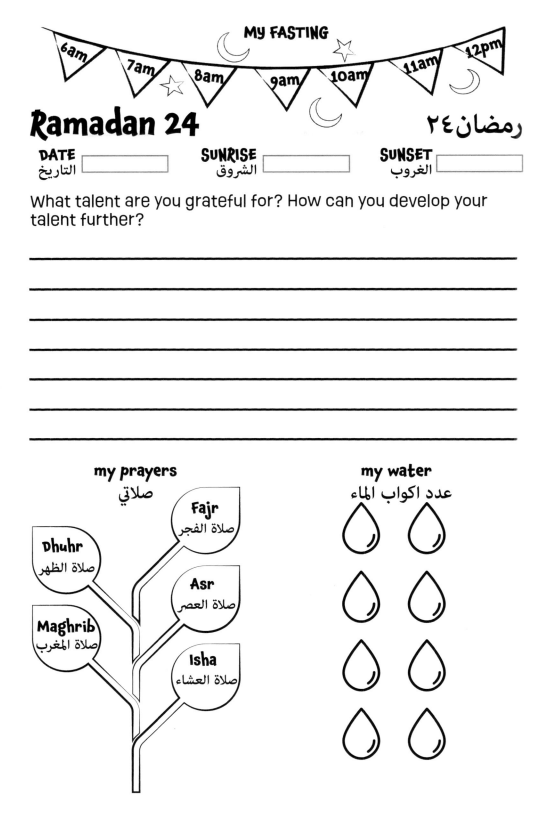

MY FASTING

6am 7am 8am 9am 10am 11am 12pm

Ramadan 24

رمضان ٢٤

DATE
التاريخ

SUNRISE
الشروق

SUNSET
الغروب

What talent are you grateful for? How can you develop your talent further?

_____

_____

_____

_____

_____

_____

my prayers
صلاتي

Fajr
صلاة الفجر

Dhuhr
صلاة الظهر

Asr
صلاة العصر

Maghrib
صلاة المغرب

Isha
صلاة العشاء

my water
عدد اكواب الماء

KenKen

puzzle 13

10 +	2 -		20 ×	
		4 ×		2 /
2 /		3 -	12 ×	
6 +				2 -
3 -		5 +		

puzzle 14

2 -	2 -		1 -	2 ×
		6 +		
2 /		5 +	6 ×	60 ×
20 ×	7 +			
			2 -	

puzzle 15

120 ×		6 +		12 ×
		2 /	7 +	
1 -	2 -			2 /
		48 ×		
2 /			2 -	

puzzle 16

1 -	2 -	5 +		1 -
		10 ×		
3 ×	2 /	15 ×		20 ×
		13 +		
			2 -	

MY FASTING

6am 7am 8am 9am 10am 11am 12pm

Ramadan 25

رمضان٢٥

DATE التاريخ _____

SUNRISE الشروق _____

SUNSET الغروب _____

What good deed did you accomplish today? How did that make you feel?

_____

_____

_____

_____

_____

_____

_____

my prayers
صلاتي

Fajr صلاة الفجر

Dhuhr صلاة الظهر

Asr صلاة العصر

Maghrib صلاة المغرب

Isha صلاة العشاء

my water
عدد اكواب الماء

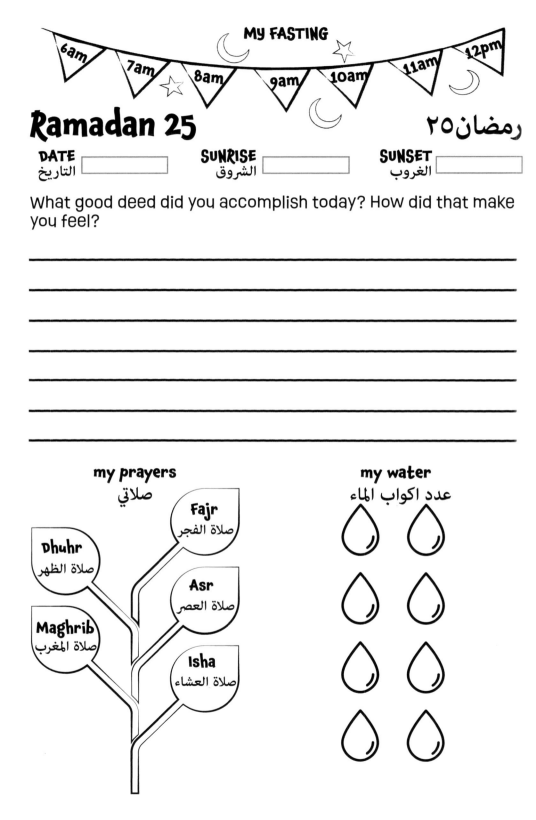

صيامي

$$\text{🪔} \times \text{🪔} = 100$$
$$\text{🪔} + \text{📖} = 26$$
$$\text{📖} - \text{🌙} = 1$$
$$\text{🪔} + \text{🌙🥤} = ?$$

$$\text{🧶} + \text{🧶} = 16$$
$$\text{🧶} \times \text{📖} = 64$$
$$\text{📖} \times \text{🌙} = 20$$
$$\text{🧶} + \text{🌙🥤} = ?$$

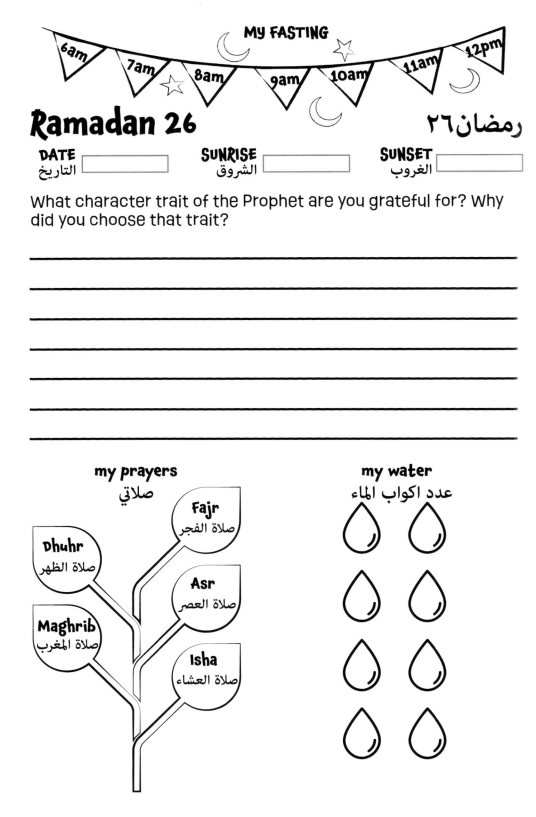

MY FASTING

6am 7am 8am 9am 10am 11am 12pm

Ramadan 26

رمضان ٢٦

DATE التاريخ

SUNRISE الشروق

SUNSET الغروب

What character trait of the Prophet are you grateful for? Why did you choose that trait?

_____

_____

_____

_____

_____

_____

my prayers
صلاتي

Fajr صلاة الفجر

Dhuhr صلاة الظهر

Asr صلاة العصر

Maghrib صلاة المغرب

Isha صلاة العشاء

my water
عدد اكواب الماء

MY FASTING

6am 7am 8am 9am 10am 11am 12pm

Ramadan 27

رمضان ٢٧

DATE التاريخ [ ]

SUNRISE الشروق [ ]

SUNSET الغروب [ ]

Draw something of a special Ramadan memory you have.

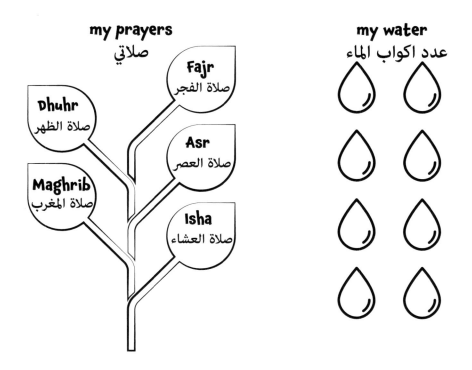

my prayers
صلاتي

Fajr صلاة الفجر

Dhuhr صلاة الظهر

Asr صلاة العصر

Maghrib صلاة المغرب

Isha صلاة العشاء

my water
عدد اكواب الماء

صيامي

1pm 2pm 3pm 4pm 5pm 6pm 7pm

puzzle 7

	6	3	4			8		5
5	9			6	1	2		3
	8	2		5			4	9
2			6			3	8	7
3	7	1	9	8	5		6	2
	4		3		7	5	9	1
			5	4	8	1	3	
8	1	6				9	7	
	3	5	1	7		9	2	

puzzle 8

2	8	4	9	6			1	3
3		7		1			9	6
9	6	1	3			8	2	7
1			6		8	7		
6	9		7	4	1		5	8
8					9		4	1
4	2			9		3	7	5
				7	3	9	8	4
	3	9		8	5	1	6	2

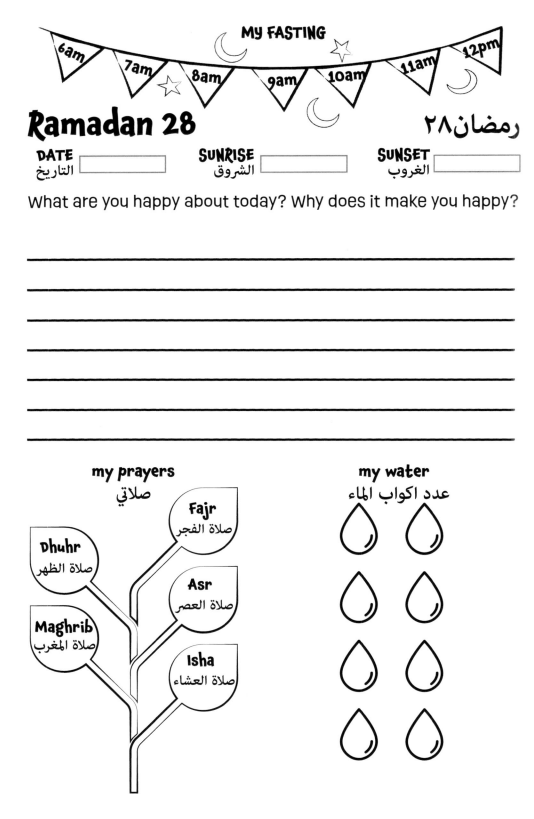

MY FASTING

6am 7am 8am 9am 10am 11am 12pm

Ramadan 28

رمضان ٢٨

DATE التاريخ

SUNRISE الشروق

SUNSET الغروب

What are you happy about today? Why does it make you happy?

_____

_____

_____

_____

_____

_____

my prayers
صلاتي

Fajr
صلاة الفجر

Dhuhr
صلاة الظهر

Asr
صلاة العصر

Maghrib
صلاة المغرب

Isha
صلاة العشاء

my water
عدد اكواب الماء

صيامي

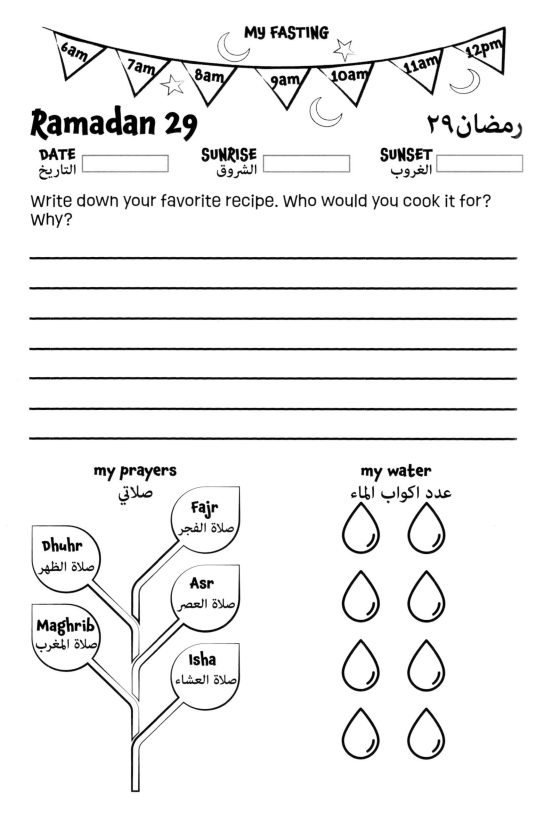

MY FASTING

6am 7am 8am 9am 10am 11am 12pm

Ramadan 29

رمضان ٢٩

DATE
التاريخ

SUNRISE
الشروق

SUNSET
الغروب

Write down your favorite recipe. Who would you cook it for? Why?

_____

_____

_____

_____

_____

_____

_____

my prayers
صلاتي

Fajr صلاة الفجر

Dhuhr صلاة الظهر

Asr صلاة العصر

Maghrib صلاة المغرب

Isha صلاة العشاء

my water
عدد اكواب الماء

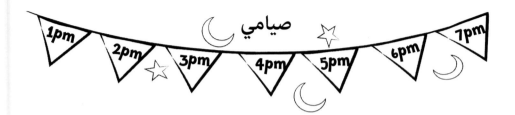

صيامي

Odd one out. Which of the images is unique?

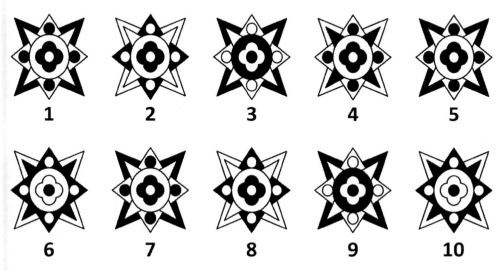

In the back. Which image is the view from the back of the row of pencils #1?

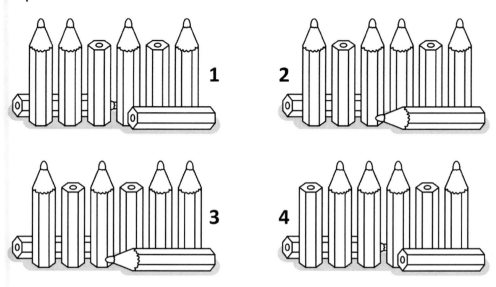

MY FASTING

6am 7am 8am 9am 10am 11am 12pm

Ramadan 30

رمضان ٣٠

DATE
التاريخ [   ]

SUNRISE
الشروق [   ]

SUNSET
الغروب [   ]

Doing acts of kindness can make a difference in the world because...

_____

_____

_____

_____

_____

_____

_____

my prayers
صلاتي

- Fajr صلاة الفجر
- Dhuhr صلاة الظهر
- Asr صلاة العصر
- Maghrib صلاة المغرب
- Isha صلاة العشاء

my water
عدد اكواب الماء

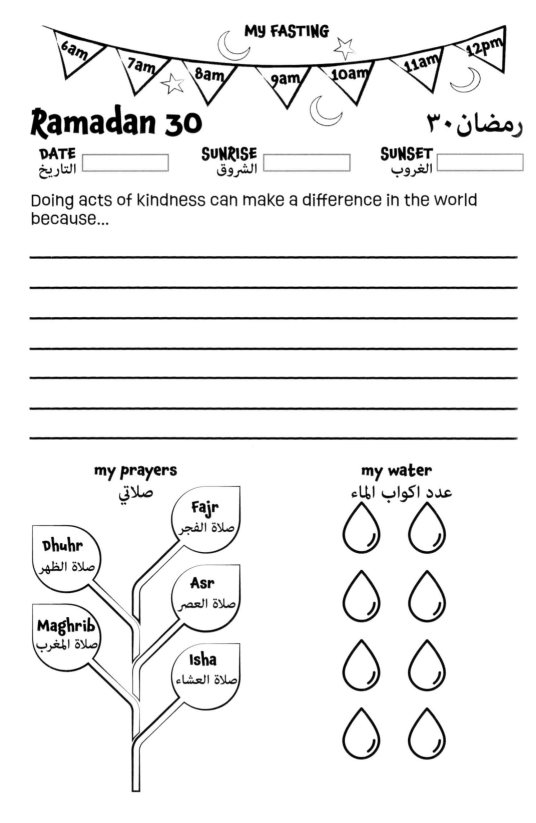

Dots and Boxes

Take turns drawing lines. The goal of this game is to be the player that completes the most boxes.

How to Play

1. Player A (heavier line) begins by drawing a horizontal or vertical line between any two adjacent dots on the grid.

2. Player B (lighter line) draws a horizontal or vertical line between any two adjacent dots on the grid.

3. When a player creates a box by drawing the fourth line, they put their initial in the box and take another turn.

4. The game is over when no more lines can be added. The winner is the who has completed the most boxes.

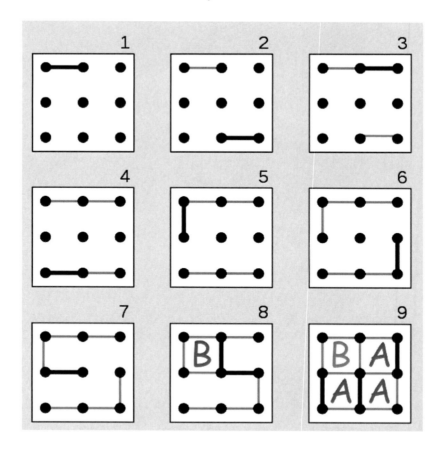

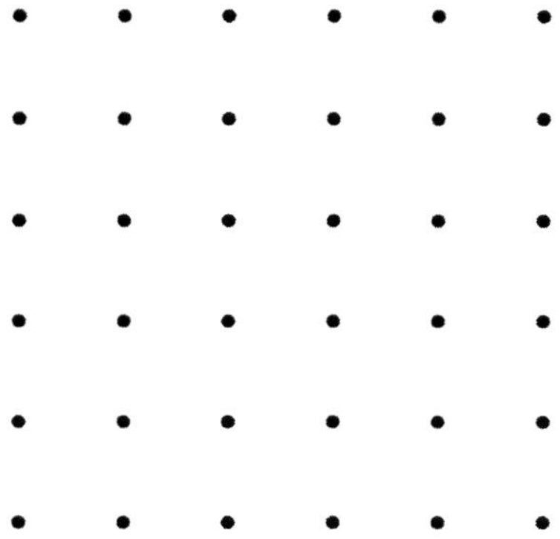

Winner: _____

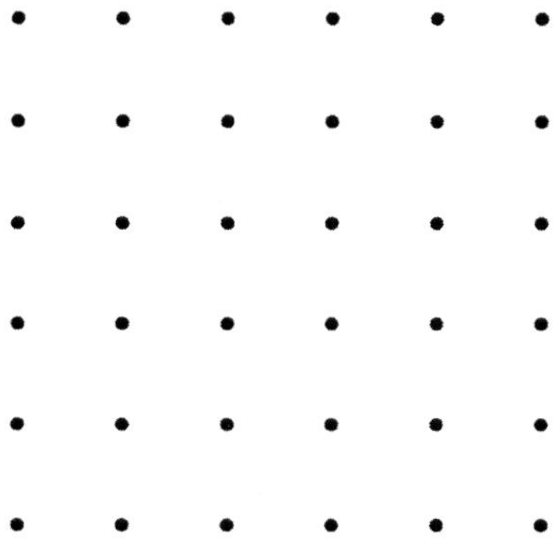

Winner: _____

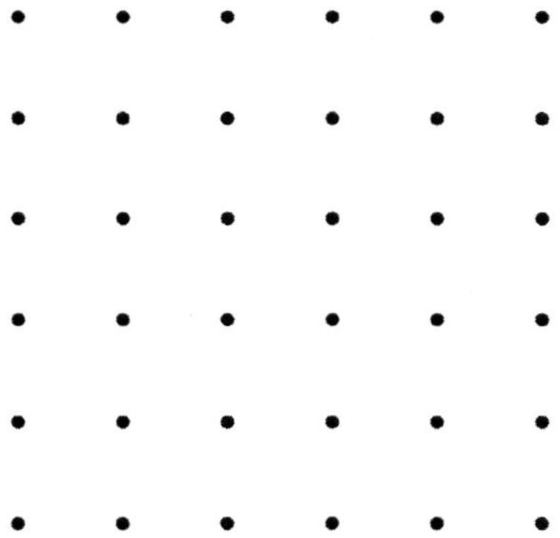

Winner: _____

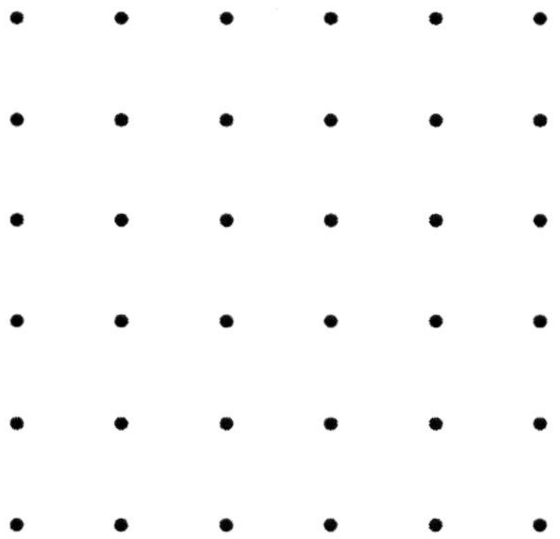

Winner: _____

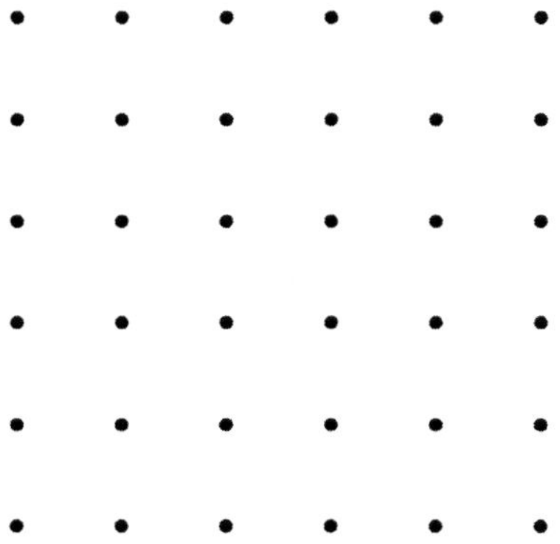

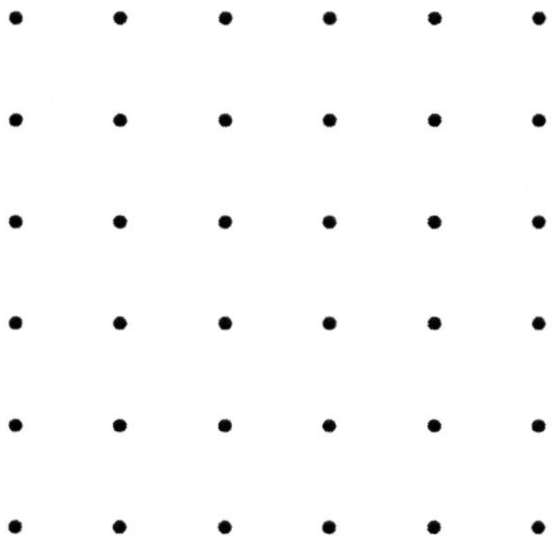

Winner: _____

Winner: _____

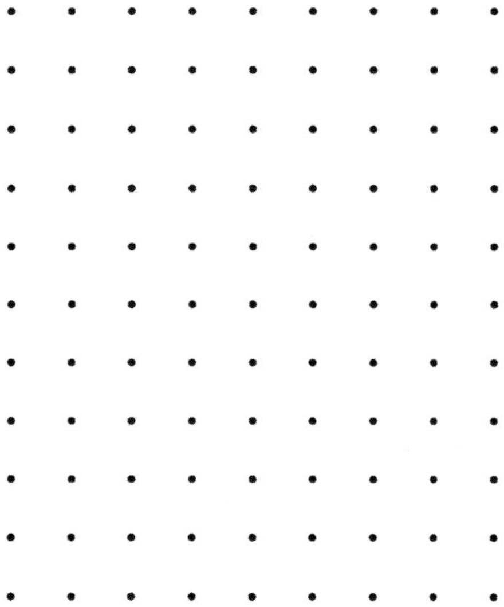

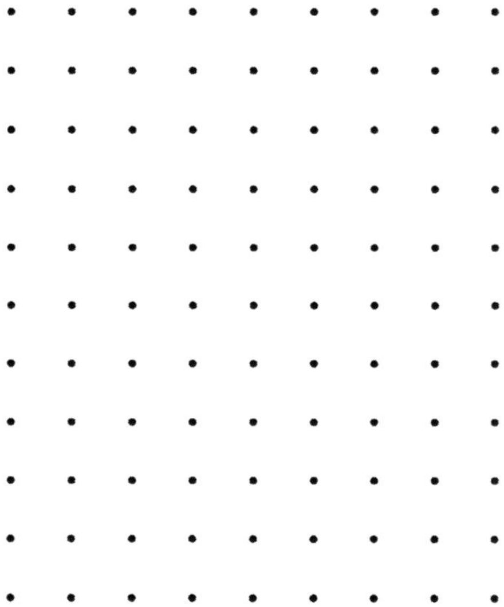

Winner: _____

Winner: _____

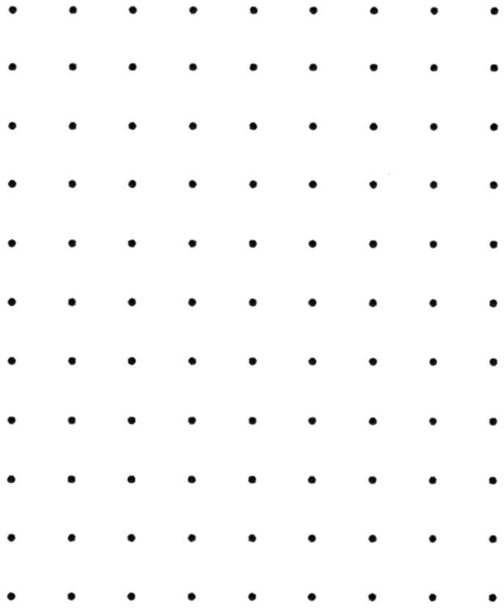

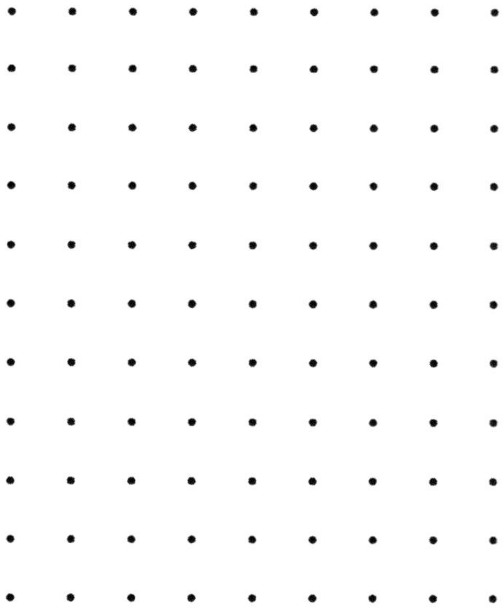

Winner: _____

Winner: _____

Winner: _____

Tic Tac Toe

Tic Tac Toe

Four in a Row

The objective is to complete a row of four X's or O's before your opponent. Use vertical, horizontal or diagonal rows.

How to Play

1. Player A starts by drawing an X in any square on the bottom row.
2. Player B places an "O" in another square on the bottom row or on top of Player A's X. The X or O must always be in the lowest row available in the column.
3. The first player to get a row of four X's or O's wins the game.

Step 1

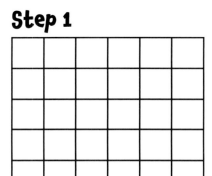

Step 2

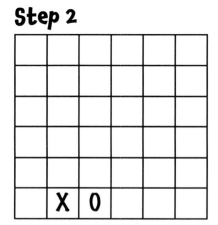

Step 3

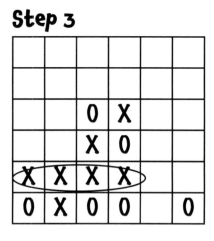

Four in a Row

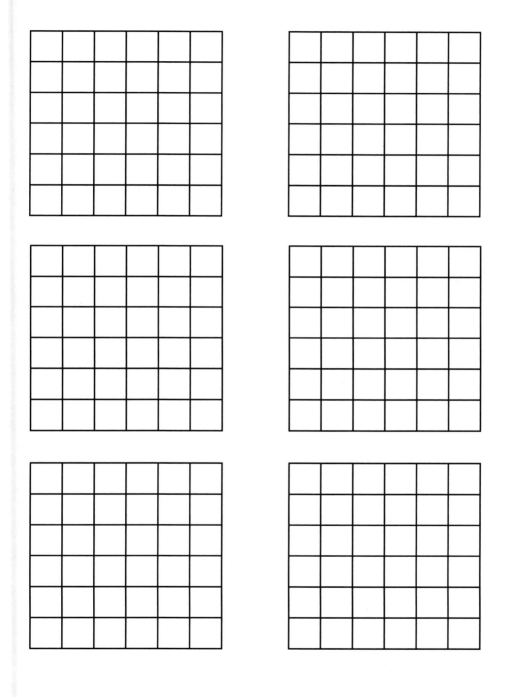

Four in a Row

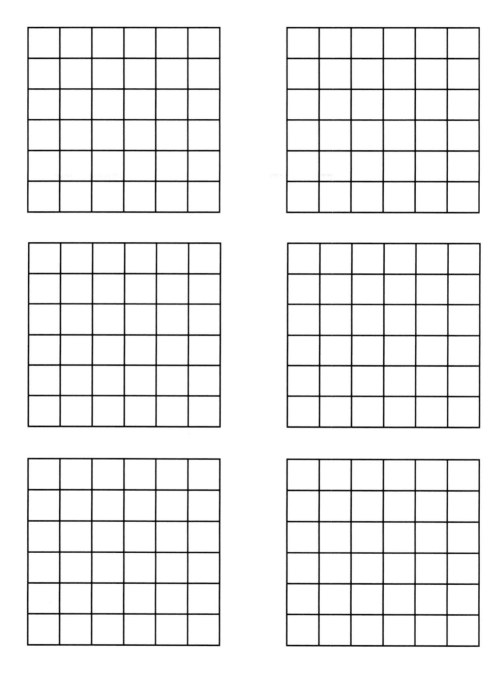

Four in a Row

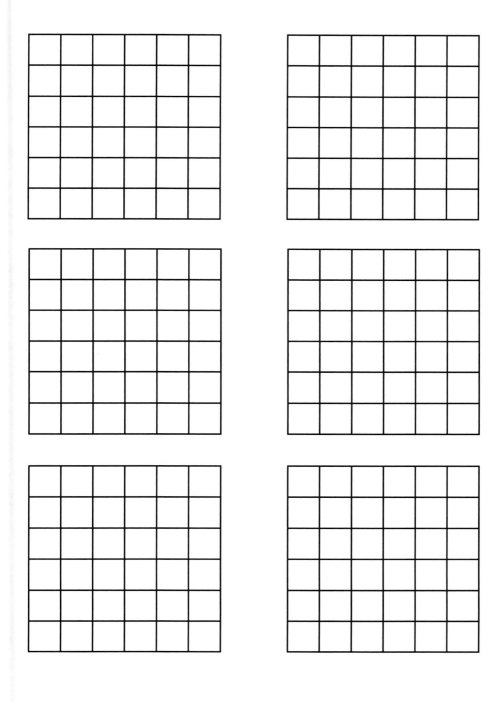

How to Play KenKen

Fill in the blank squares so that each row and each column contain all of the digits 1 thru 4. The heavy lines indicate areas called cages. These contain groups of numbers that can be combined (in any order) to produce the result shown in the cage using the indicated math operation. For example, 12× means you can multiply the numbers together to produce 12. Numbers in cages may repeat, as long as they are not in the same row or column.

Example

1. In the top left (5+) cage, you can have the combination of 3+2 or 4+1. In the cage below (6+), you can only have the combination of 1+2+3. Since 1, 2 and 3 are used in column 1, the top left number must be 4. That means cage 5+ must have 4 and then 1.

2. In the 9+ cage, the top numbers must be 3 and 2 (to keep the numbers 1-4 in the row). That means the second row must be 3 and 1 (3+2+3+1=9). The 3's must be in different columns, so it will be either 3 and 2 with 1 and 3 below, or 2 and 3 with 3 and 1 below.

   To figure out which it is, look at the 5+ cage at the bottom. The numbers in the 4th column must be 1, 2, 3 and 4. If the top numbers are 2 and 3, the bottom numbers must be 3 and 1. That means only 4 and 2 are left in the column. Since these numbers need to add up to 5, this can't be right. So, the top numbers must be 3 and 2 and the bottom numbers are 1 and 3.

Start

5 +		9 +	
6 +	10 +		
			5 +
	1 -		

Step 1

5 + 4	1	9 +	
6 +	10 +		
			5 +
	1 -		

Step 2

5 + 4	1	9 + 3	2
6 +	10 +	1	3
			5 +
	1 -		

3. In the second row, the 2 empty boxes must be 2 and 4. Since there is already a 4 in the first column, the 2 must belong there and the 4 goes into the second column.
4. In the 10+ cage, the sum of the remaining numbers must be 6 (6+4=10). That can only be done with the combination of 4 and 2 or 3 and 3. Since column 3 already has 3, it must be 4 and 2. Since column 2 already has a 4, so the 2 goes here.
5. Then the middle columns can be completed with 3 and 2.
   The 5+ cage can now be completed with the 4 and 1. Because of the other numbers in the 3rd row, they must be placed with the 1 at the top of the cage followed by the 4. And then the final numbers can be placed.

Step 3

5 + 4	1	9 + 3	2
6 + 2	10 + 4	1	3
	2	4	5 +
	1 - 		

Step 4

5 + 4	1	9 + 3	2
6 + 2	10 + 4	1	3
	2	4	5 +
	1 - 3	2	

Step 5

5 + 4	1	9 + 3	2
6 + 2	10 + 4	1	3
3	2	4	5 + 1
1	1 - 3	2	4

How to Play Sudoku

Sudoku means "single number" in Japanese. A classic Sudoku grid has 81 cells (9 rows by 9 columns). The grid is subdivided into 9 blocks, each 3x3 containing 9 cells.

The objective is to fill the grid with the numbers 1 to 9 so that each column, each row, and each of the nine 3×3 grids contains all of the digits from 1 to 9. For example:

6	4	2	5	3	8	9	1	7
7	9	3	2	6	1	5	8	4
1	8	5	4	7	9	2	3	6
3	7	1	9	5	6	4	2	8
2	6	9	8	1	4	7	5	3
8	5	4	3	2	7	1	6	9
9	2	6	1	4	3	8	7	5
4	1	7	6	8	5	3	9	2
5	3	8	7	9	2	6	4	1

Puzzle Solving Techniques

There are several techniques to solve a Sudoku puzzle. Start with scanning. Look across a row, column and 3x3 block to identify where you can find the "only possible number" that fits. For example, look at the cell where there is a STAR. The only number that fits in this cell is a 5 because the columns to the left and right have 5s in them. And the rows above and below already have a 5. That means the 5 is the only number that fits in that cell.

You can also look for the "only possible cell". In the example, look at the cell with the diamond. The 2 rows below both have a 2 in them, so this cell is the only place where a 2 can fit.

Remember, no number from 1 to 9 can be repeated in any row, column or 3x3 grid.

6	4		5	3		9	1	7
7	9					5	8	4
	8	5	4				3	6
3	7			5	6			
2	6			1		★		3
8	5	4	3		7			9
9	◆	6	1	4		8		5
				8	5	3	9	2
			7		2	6	4	

How to Solve Math Picture Puzzles

Rules

1. All characters have different answers, e.g., 1, 2, 3

2. All characters are whole numbers, e.g., 1 or 5 (not 1.5 or 2/3)

3. Multiple characters on the same space are added together, e.g., 2 characters which are 5 each => 5 + 5 = 10

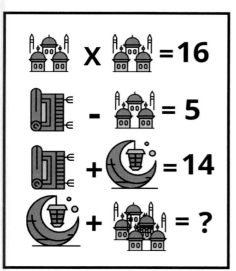

Example

From the first equation, 16/2 = 8, so a mosque = 8.

1. Mat - 8 = 5. What number does the mat have to be? 13

2. A mat plus an crescent = 14. Since the mat is 13, 13 + crescent = 14. That means the crescent = 1

3. Crescent plus 2 mosque = ? 1 plus 8 + 8 = 17

Sudoku Solutions

puzzle 1

3	8	6	5	2	1	4	7	9
1	5	4	7	9	3	6	2	8
2	9	7	6	4	8	5	3	1
9	7	5	3	8	2	1	6	4
8	4	3	1	6	5	2	9	7
6	1	2	9	7	4	8	5	3
4	3	1	2	5	9	7	8	6
7	2	8	4	3	6	9	1	5
5	6	9	8	1	7	3	4	2

puzzle 2

2	5	6	8	9	1	3	4	7
8	3	7	2	4	6	5	1	9
9	1	4	7	3	5	8	6	2
1	9	3	5	8	7	4	2	6
5	7	2	4	6	3	1	9	8
4	6	8	1	2	9	7	5	3
3	2	1	9	5	8	6	7	4
7	8	9	6	1	4	2	3	5
6	4	5	3	7	2	9	8	1

puzzle 3

8	4	6	5	9	2	1	7	3
1	7	3	6	4	8	9	2	5
5	2	9	7	3	1	6	4	8
6	9	4	3	2	5	8	1	7
3	8	1	4	6	7	2	5	9
2	5	7	8	1	9	4	3	6
7	1	5	9	8	4	3	6	2
4	6	8	2	5	3	7	9	1
9	3	2	1	7	6	5	8	4

puzzle 4

4	2	1	5	3	8	9	7	6
3	5	7	9	2	6	1	8	4
9	6	8	4	7	1	5	2	3
6	4	9	3	1	2	8	5	7
7	1	3	8	4	5	2	6	9
5	8	2	6	9	7	4	3	1
8	7	5	1	6	9	3	4	2
1	3	6	2	5	4	7	9	8
2	9	4	7	8	3	6	1	5

puzzle 5

4	2	3	8	1	9	5	7	6
7	8	1	6	5	2	3	9	4
5	9	6	3	4	7	2	8	1
9	5	8	1	3	6	4	2	7
2	6	4	7	9	5	1	3	8
3	1	7	2	8	4	9	6	5
6	7	9	5	2	1	8	4	3
8	4	5	9	6	3	7	1	2
1	3	2	4	7	8	6	5	9

puzzle 6

7	9	3	4	8	2	5	6	1
2	8	1	9	5	6	3	7	4
6	5	4	3	7	1	9	2	8
8	7	6	5	2	3	1	4	9
1	2	5	7	4	9	6	8	3
4	3	9	1	6	8	7	5	2
3	4	7	2	1	5	8	9	6
5	1	8	6	9	4	2	3	7
9	6	2	8	3	7	4	1	5

puzzle 7

7	6	3	4	9	2	8	1	5
5	9	4	8	6	1	2	7	3
1	8	2	7	5	3	6	4	9
2	5	9	6	1	4	3	8	7
3	7	1	9	8	5	4	6	2
6	4	8	3	2	7	5	9	1
9	2	7	5	4	8	1	3	6
8	1	6	2	3	9	7	5	4
4	3	5	1	7	6	9	2	8

puzzle 8

2	8	4	9	6	7	5	1	3
3	5	7	8	1	2	4	9	6
9	6	1	3	5	4	8	2	7
1	4	5	6	2	8	7	3	9
6	9	3	7	4	1	2	5	8
8	7	2	5	3	9	6	4	1
4	2	8	1	9	6	3	7	5
5	1	6	2	7	3	9	8	4
7	3	9	4	8	5	1	6	2

KenKen Solutions

puzzle 1

2	4	3	1
1	3	2	4
4	2	1	3
3	1	4	2

puzzle 2

3	2	4	1
4	1	3	2
1	3	2	4
2	4	1	3

puzzle 3

2	3	4	1
1	2	3	4
4	1	2	3
3	4	1	2

puzzle 4

3	1	2	4
4	3	1	2
1	2	4	3
2	4	3	1

puzzle 5

3	2	1	4
1	4	2	3
2	3	4	1
4	1	3	2

puzzle 6

4	3	2	1
2	1	3	4
3	4	1	2
1	2	4	3

puzzle 7

3	4	1	2
1	3	2	4
2	1	4	3
4	2	3	1

puzzle 8

2	1	4	3
1	3	2	4
3	4	1	2
4	2	3	1

puzzle 9

4	2	5	3	1
1	4	3	2	5
3	5	4	1	2
2	3	1	5	4
5	1	2	4	3

puzzle 10

1	2	4	5	3
2	1	5	3	4
3	4	1	2	5
4	5	3	1	2
5	3	2	4	1

puzzle 11

2	4	1	3	5
1	2	3	5	4
4	1	5	2	3
3	5	4	1	2
5	3	2	4	1

puzzle 12

5	2	1	4	3
4	1	5	3	2
3	5	2	1	4
1	3	4	2	5
2	4	3	5	1

puzzle 13

2	3	1	5	4
3	5	4	1	2
4	2	5	3	1
5	1	2	4	3
1	4	3	2	5

puzzle 14

1	3	5	4	2
3	4	2	5	1
2	1	4	3	5
4	5	1	2	3
5	2	3	1	4

puzzle 15

2	4	5	1	3
3	5	1	2	4
4	3	2	5	1
5	1	3	4	2
1	2	4	3	5

puzzle 16

5	3	1	4	2
4	1	5	2	3
1	2	3	5	4
3	4	2	1	5
2	5	4	3	1

Math Picture Puzzle Solutions

5 X **5** = 25

5 + **3** = 8

12 - **3** = 9

5 + **24** = 29

---

7 X **7** = 49

7 + **4** = 11

5 - **4** = 1

7 + **10** = 17

---

12 X **12** = 144

12 + **11** = 23

11 - **3** = 8

12 + **6** = 18

---

12 + **12** = 24

16 X **12** = 192

8 X **6** = 48

24 + **6** = 30

---

10 X **10** = 100

10 + **16** = 26

8 - **7** = 1

10 + **14** = 24

---

8 + **8** = 16

8 X **8** = 64

4 X **5** = 20

8 + **10** = 18

Made in United States
North Haven, CT
06 March 2023

33665425R00046